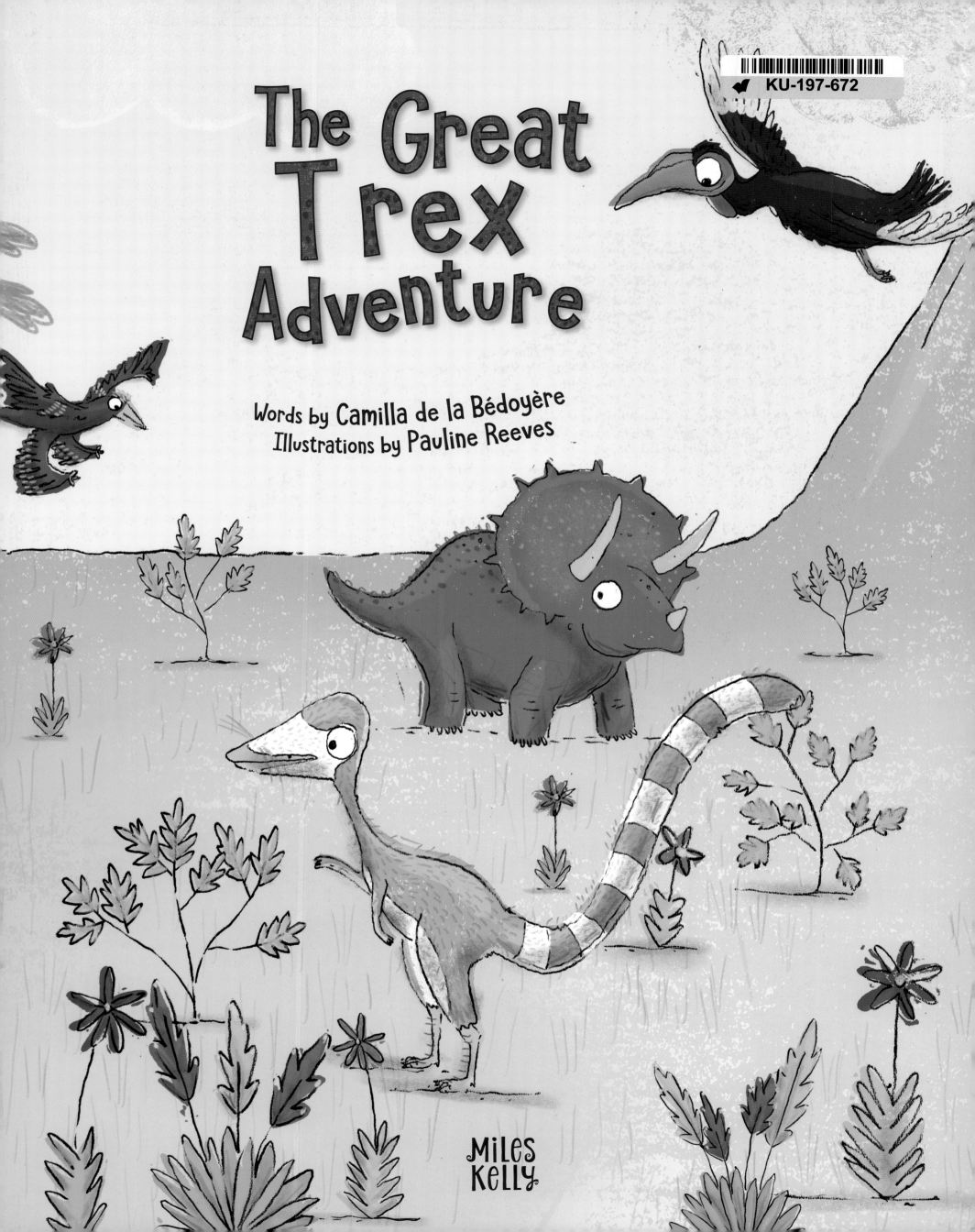

The Great Trex Adventure

Words by Camilla de la Bédoyère
Illustrations by Pauline Reeves

MILES
KELLY

Hello!

I'm Peter.
There are lots of animals to spot here, but I'm on the hunt for dinosaurs. **T rex** is the best!

First published in 2019 by Miles Kelly Publishing Ltd
Harding's Barn, Bardfield End Green, Thaxted, Essex, CM6 3PX, UK

Copyright © Miles Kelly Publishing Ltd 2019

2 4 6 8 10 9 7 5 3 1

Publishing Director Belinda Gallagher
Creative Director Jo Cowan
Editorial Director Rosie Neave
Design Manager Simon Lee
Image Manager Liberty Newton
Production Elizabeth Collins, Jennifer Brunwin-Jones
Reprographics Stephan Davis, Callum Ratcliffe-Bingham
Assets Lorraine King

ISBN 978-1-78617-832-9

Printed in China

British Library Cataloguing-in-Publication Data
A catalogue record for this book is available from the British Library

Made with paper from a sustainable forest

www.mileskelly.net

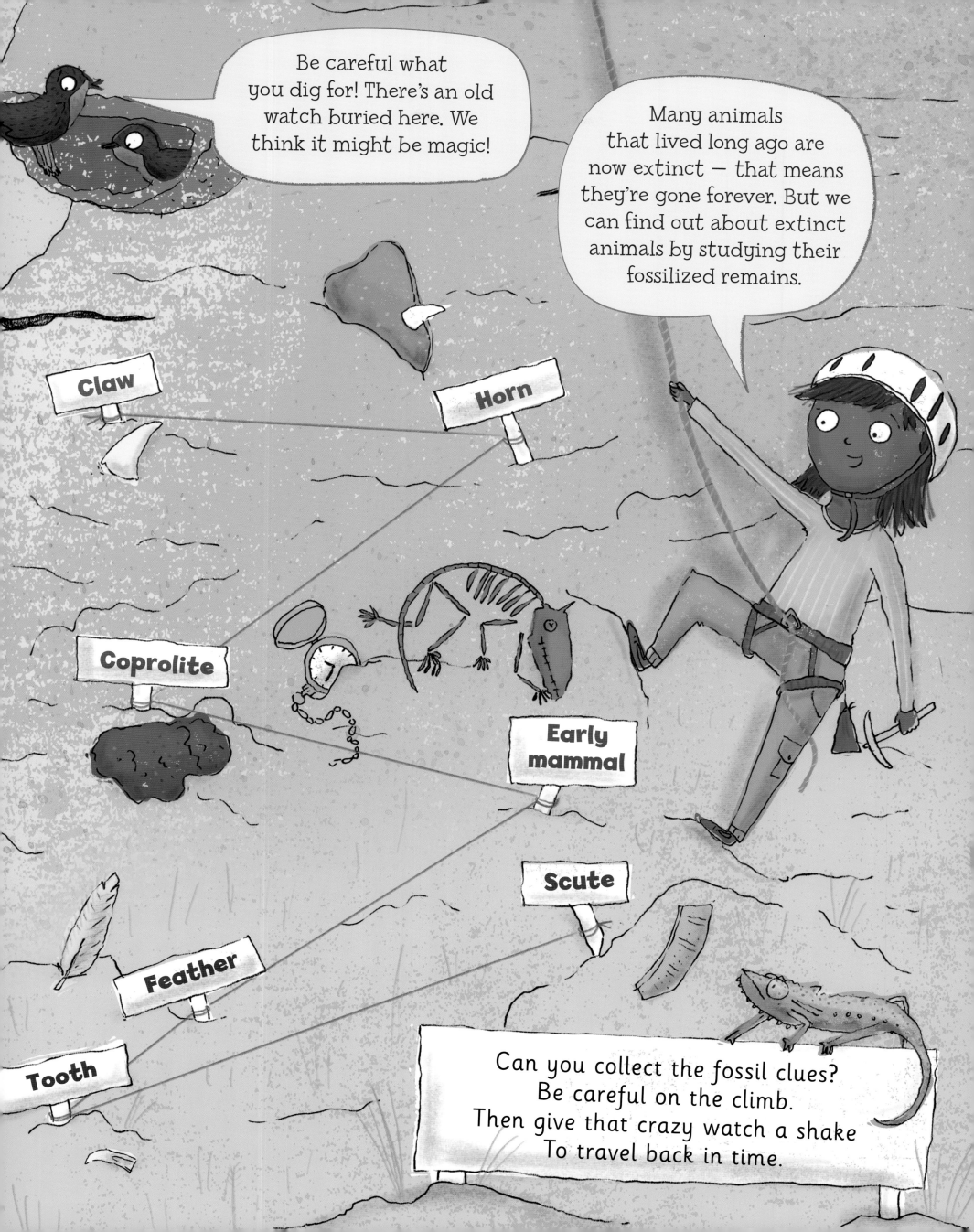

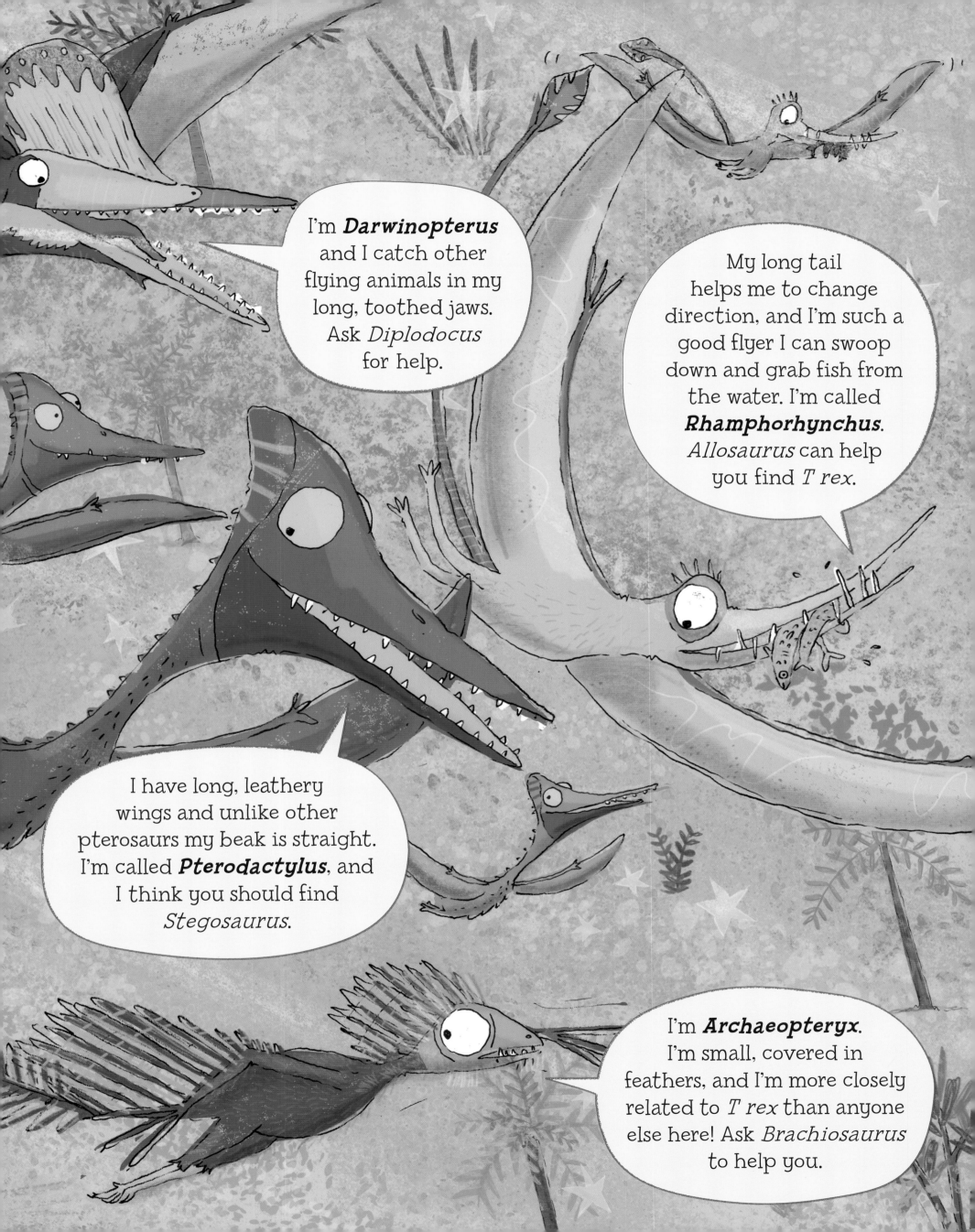

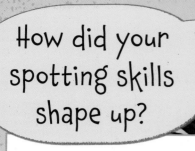

You've been on an adventure,
Meeting creatures on the way,
Tick the boxes if you saw them,
When you finish, shout "Hooray!"

Placerias ☐

Riojasaurus ☐

Melanorosaurus ☐

Postosuchus ☐

Giant dicynodont ☐

Triadobatrachus ☐

Archaeolepis mane ☐

Scelidosaurus ☐

Baryonyx ☐

Iguanodon ☐

Microraptor ☐

Hesperornis ☐

Pteranodon ☐

Ammonite ☐

Stygimoloch ☐

Stegoceras ☐

Acanthisitta ☐

Quetzalcoatlus ☐

Velociraptor ☐

Ichthyornis ☐